The Whole Truth

Five Green Bottles

by Ray Jenkins

Nelson

Thomas Nelson and Sons Ltd
Nelson House Mayfield Road
Walton-on-Thames Surrey
KT12 5PL UK

Nelson Blackie
Wester Cleddens Road
Bishopbriggs
Glasgow
G64 2NZ

Thomas Nelson (Hong Kong) Ltd
Toppan Building 10/F
22a Westlands Road
Quarry Bay Hong Kong

Thomas Nelson Australia
102 Dodds Street
South Melbourne
Victoria 3205   Australia

Nelson Canada
1120 Birchmount Road
Scarborough Ontario
M1K 5G4   Canada

© Ray Jenkins: *Five Green Bottles* 1968 and 1975;
The Whole Truth 1969 and 1975

First published by Macmillan Education Ltd 1975
ISBN 0-333-15022-8

This edition published by Thomas Nelson and Sons Ltd 1992

ISBN 0-17-432452-9
NPN 9 8 7 6 5

FOREWORD

DRAMASCRIPTS are intended for use in secondary schools, amateur theatrical groups and youth clubs, and some will be enjoyed by young people who are still at primary school. They may be used in a variety of ways: read privately for pleasure or aloud in groups; acted in the classroom, church hall or youth club, or in public performances.

These two plays by Ray Jenkins – THE WHOLE TRUTH and FIVE GREEN BOTTLES – are intended for senior pupils, rather than the very young, but they will have a wide appeal.

THE WHOLE TRUTH is described by the author as 'a play for the classroom'. It shows a group of fourteen-year-old boys and girls who have been asked by their teacher to organise a classroom court. As they set this up, they find out, almost by accident, that one of their number has, in fact, recently appeared in a real court on a criminal charge. Her story, as it is re-enacted in the 'mock' trial, is intensely moving.

In FIVE GREEN BOTTLES, which is set in an ordinary household, we meet the members of a family when they are caught up in the normal early-morning rush of breakfast-and-get-out. The drama comes from the inability of the mother to understand her sons and daughter. ('Kids. You have them, you raise them and then, one day, before you can turn round, you don't know them. They might as well be Zulus.') It is a memorable play.

GUY WILLIAMS
Advisory Editor

CONTENTS

THE CHARACTERS

Boys
  MASON
  BERNARD
  JOHN
  PINKY
  LARRY
  BARRY
  SIMON

Girls
  GLENDA
  BILLIE
  JOAN
  DENISE
  PEARL
  MAVIS

Teacher
  MISS BRYANT

In the Court

The Bench	DENISE, PINKY, LARRY
Clerk	BILLIE
Probation Officers	PEARL, MAVIS
Education Officer	JOHN
Policemen	BARRY, SIMON
Usher	BERNARD

Mother
  GLENDA

THE WHOLE TRUTH

(A classroom, full of annoyed bustle. The class of fourteen-year-olds has just been given an assignment.)

Mason. No – shut up! Give us a chance! We've got to get organised!
Glenda. You couldn't organise a pack of brownies!
Mason. She said I'm in charge – all right?
Glenda. She must be mad.
Mason. Look, Noddy, back in your box!
Glenda *(sweetly)*. Please sir, we know a good lake you could jump into.
Mason. Quiet! Keep quiet!

(Other voices shout 'shut up', 'we ain't got time', 'lay off', etc ...)

Come on! You're a load a' screaming cripples!
Billie *(sharply)*. Cripples don't shout.
Mason *(chastened)*. I know they don't.
Billie. Then don't say they do.
Mason. Look, know-all –
Billie. You don't know anything.
Mason. And you do, I suppose?
Billie. I know more than you.
Mason. Take over then!
Billie. Why should I?
Mason. All right then – when I want your help I'll ask for it – till then
    BELT UP!

(This shout is in almost complete silence. The class has been listening to the argument.)

Brilliant! You don't half take some organising.

(Silence.)

John. Silence reigns and we all get wet.

(Sniggers.)

Bernard *(horror)*. I've got WEB FEET!
Glenda. You know your trouble, Bernard.
John. He doesn't wash between his toes.

(Delighted laughter.)

Glenda *(moaning)*. You're a moaner.
Mason. I'll give you three! ONE ...
All. TWO!

(Silence.)

Mason. Three ... Right,

(Silence.)

Point is, what do we do?

(Pause.)

Glenda. Come on then you're organising!
Mason. I can't when you don't give me a chance can I, you silly moo!
Joan. We've got to get a court going, Miss Bryant said –
Mason. I know what she said – 'I want a court, any court, and I want
      you to organise it, with proper judges and that, and a case for the
      persecution – we all heard it.
Billie. Prosecution.
Mason. Thas what I said.
Billie. You said 'persecution'.
Mason. IT'S THE SAME THING! Right.

(Pause.)

A proper court.

(Pause.)

Any ideas?

2

(Pause. Someone sniffs.)

Come on, wash your heads out – look she'll be back in ten minutes! A court!

Joan. How can we, when we haven't been in one?

Mason. Then you haven't lived.

Glenda. Well, seeing you have been in one – you tell us.

Mason. Who said I been in one?

Joan *(timid)*. You did.

Mason. Point out to me the time when I said I did, mouse!

Joan. You gave the impression.

Glenda. Well, have you?

Mason. What about all the others?

Glenda. Have you?

(Pause.)

Mason. Not exactly.

Glenda. Have you?

(Pause.)

Mason. No!

(Laughter.)

But if you don't stop getting at me I'll be there for murder.

Glenda. You're all talk.

Mason. But I know what it's like.

Glenda. Tell us then.

Mason. If you'll listen I will.

Glenda. I'm all ears.

Mason. I always knew there was something wrong with you! Right.

(He's got them. Silence.)

My brother's been up. HE told me.

Larry. My cousin's been up.

Mason *(relieved)*. Good, Larry, you can check me when I goes wrong.

Larry. But he said he was so scared he didn't see nothing or hear nothing. He got remand. Third time.

Mason. He must've heard the judge!

Larry. You don't have judges in a juvenile court –

John. You have bus conductors!

Larry. You have magistrates.

Mason. I know, you have *three*.

Larry. And the one in the middle's a lady.

Mason. Right – wrap a towel round your middle and you'll be all right then, missus.

Larry. I'm not acting.

Mason. Then we'll have to have old Dracula!

Glenda. I hate you!

(Pause.)

Pinky. Old Andrews 4D was had s-stealing a l-lampost.

(Bursts of sniggers and laughs.)

He s-said it's a l-lady m-magistrate. The old coots who're all old and d-don't l-like kids send you to p-prison. And they d-draw di-di-nosaurs on the b-blotting p-paper when they're d-doing it.

(Pause.)

Mason. Lovely speech, Pinky. Now can we get on with it. And for a start-off, seeing you knows all about it, you can be the judge.

Larry. Magistrate.

Pinky. I d-don't w-want to be.

Mason. I'm in charge.

Pinky. My d-dad says d-don't join anything.

Mason. And my dad says if it moves salute it. You're appointed. Right, we want a woman.

Denise. Me!

Mason. Charming! Right, you sit in the middle. Pinky and Larry're the other two judges.

(Chairs scrape as they move and resettle.)

4

Larry. How did he get a lamp-post? ...
Pinky. He t-tied it to his b-bike.
Denise *(hammering).* Guilty! Ninety-nine years!
Larry. What for?
Denise *(giggling).* I dunno!

*(**Mason** is moving around, still organising.)*

Mason. Now what – yes – we want a dock and a couple of coppers who don't say anything.
Simon. Me.
Barry. Me.
Mason. Right – Barry – you and Si – at the side.
Barry. What do we do?
Mason. What you're told and not in your helmets.

(They march off.)

Where does the public sit?

(No reply.)

Right – at the back.

(There is a thunderous noise as the whole class rushes to the back. Chairs and desks crash.)

NOT ALL OF YOU! NITS! We've got to get all the people in the court yet!

(They settle back in their chairs.)

Larry. Mason.
Mason. Yes, your worship?
Larry. My cousin said there ain't anybody from the public.
Mason. Well, there is here – hundreds of them!

(The public benches cheer and stamp their feet.)

5

Mason. What else, Larry?

Larry. The reporters can't write your names in the papers.

Pinky. P-probation officers.

Mason. How many?

Pinky. T-two.

Mason. Right, two volunteers, you and you.

(Two girls giggle.)

Mavis. Go on, Pearl.

Pearl. No.

Mavis. For a giggle.

Pearl. Only if I don't have to say anything.

Mason. Marvellous. Two probation officers and they don't say anything. How would you like it if you had a dumb probation officer!

Mavis *(giggling)*. What do they do?

Mason. You have to listen in court, then if I'm put on probation you have to come round our house and check I'm in.

Pearl. I'm not coming round your house. I'll never know where I've been.

Mavis. Where do we go?

Mason. In the middle, in front of the judges.

(They giggle to their places. Sporadic applause.)

Who else?

Larry. Scarper Flo.

Mason. Is she there?

Larry. She was for our Vincent.

Mason. We want a truant officer.

Denise *(hammering)*. What about it if the case isn't about truanting?

Larry. You still have to have somebody from the Education.

Mason. That means somebody thick.

John. Me.

Mason. Right, Lady Flo, with the other lot in front of Pinky's lot. Right – thas about all, then.

Denise. Who's being tried?

Mason. Me.

(Groans.)

6

Watch it!

Pinky. What've y-you done?

Larry. What's the charge?

Mason. Pinching.

Billie. What?

Mason. I'm thinking.

Glenda. Wonders never cease!

Larry (*to* **Pinky**). What did old Andrews get for the lamp-posts?

Pinky. Th-three quid.

(*Sniggers.*)

Billie. You're all wrong. You've missed something.

(*Silence.*)

Mason. It's still alive! What have we missed, O know-all?

Billie. The clerk.

(*Pause.*)

Mason. Who's he?

Billie. He tells the court all about the law.

Mason. When they've got three magistrates?

Billie. They're amateurs. They're only part-time.

(*Silence except for occasional fidgets.*)

Mason. How do you know?

Billie. I've been there.

(*Restlessness stops.*)

Mason (*impressed*). How many times?

Billie. Two.

(*Pause.*)

Mason. Thas why they've put you down with us lot?

7

(Pause.)

You was had up?
Billie. I said.
Mason. What for?

(Pause.)

Billie. I-I can't tell you.
Larry. 'Can't' or 'won't'?
Billie *(screaming)*. WON'T!

(Utter silence.)

Mason *(gently)*. S'all right, we're only playing.

(Pause.)

Billie. All right, I'll be the clerk. I sit near the magistrates. Then the
　　usher –
John. Who's he?
Billie. Police.
Barry. Us?
Billie. No – in plain clothes.
Bernard. I'll be that.
Billie. You call out the number of the case and the prisoner's brought in.
Mason. OK we'll do that – do they have handcuffs?
Billie. No.
Mason *(disappointed)*. Oh.
Billie *(gradually speaking with more and more authority)*. You come in
　　with your father – or your mother. And usually she's crying so
　　they have a box of paper hankies by the witness-stand. That's a
　　box facing the bench.
Denise *(filled with awe)*. What's the bench?
Billie. You're the bench – the magistrates.
Pinky. Who g-goes into the b-box?

(Pause.)

Billie. The policewoman.

8

Larry. What for?
Billie *(low)*. She tells the court what you've done.

(Silence.)

Mason *(deliberately to break the tension)*. Right – I'm coming in.
Bernard. Hang on – wait for me – I'm supposed to be bringing *you* in!

(They exit and re-enter and march to a stop.)

Mason. I swear to tell the truth, the whole truth –
Billie. THEY DON'T USE THE DOCK!

(Pause.)

(calmer) You stand in front of the Bench.

*(***Mason** *steps out of the witness box.)*

And the usher says – 'Here's . . . whatever your first name is . . . '
Mason *(pause)*. Daniel.
Billie. Here's Daniel, Your Worship, and this is his mother.
Bernard. Here's Daniel, Your Worship, and we haven't got a mother.
Billie. You have to have someone with you.
Glenda. I'll be his mum.

(Wolf-whistles from the public benches.)

Mason. Not on your flaming life –
Glenda *(enjoying herself)*. Wait till I get you home my boy, you'll get a
    thing or two coming to you, dragging me down here – the shame
    of it! Soon as your dad gets in from the pub you'll be racing up
    and down a few stairs –
Mason. Oh shut up, Dracula!

*(***Glenda** *cuffs him.)*

Glenda. Don't you talk to your mother like that, my boy!
Mason *(murderous)*. I'll get you!
Glenda *(sweetly)*. S'all right, we're only playing!

Billie. The point is – what've you done?

Mason. I dunno – maybe a scooter – or is that too hard?

Billie. Depends.

Mason. No – don't you have to know the law, you know, what I've contrabanded?

*(**Billie** turns away.)*

Billie *(finally)*. If it's to do with ... taking things – then I know it. I don't ... know anything else.

(Silence. Everyone is impressed.)

Mason. So?

Billie. Say you've ... stolen a knife.

(Pause.)

Pinky. Knives a–aren't all–allowed in school.

Mason. I got one.

(He produces it triumphantly.)

Here!

(Pause.)

Billie. It's ... brand-new.

(He sticks it into the 'bench' table. Somebody gasps.)

Denise. Exhibit 'A'.

(She hammers smartly.)

And everybody keep their hands off it. You and all, Larry!

Billie *(pause)*. Come in again.

*(**Mason** goes out.)*

Mason. Come on, Mum!

(Glenda hurries out.)

Billie *(whispers)*. Call out the number.
Bernard *(whispers)*. Uh – Case Number Twenty-Three.
Billie *(whispers)*. To the court!
Bernard *(bellowing)*. Case Number Twenty-Three!
Denise. Bring them in, usher.

(Bernard collects Mason and Glenda, who is sniffing. They stand before the bench.)

Bernard. This is Daniel, Your Worship, and this is Mother.
Billie. Sit down, Mother.

(Glenda sits.)

Now Daniel.
Mason. Yes, miss.
Billie. Age?
Mason. Fourteen.
Billie *(rustling paper)*. You're charged with stealing a knife from Smith's Knife Shop. Do you know what that means?
Mason. Yes.
Billie. Now, you can be tried by a jury, sometime next month, or you can be dealt with by these magistrates. Which do you want?
Mason. Here.
Billie. Do you admit you took the knife?
Mason. Prove it!
Billie *(naturally)*. No! They tell you to plead guilty! It saves bother!

(Pause.)

Mason. Yes. I took it.
Billie *(to Denise)*. Now you ask – who can give us the facts?
Denise *(self-consciously)*. Who can give us the facts?

(Silence. Somebody stifles a snigger.)

Billie. There's got to be the police. They've got to prosecute, to tell the court.

(Silence.)

Pinky. Wh-what d-do we d-do now?
Mason. Thas your bother, mate.
Larry. *You're* on trial!
Mason. Persecute me, then!
Denise. Make something up!
Mason. Why me?
Denise. If we don't know what you've done we can't go on.
Mason. Alwis me!
Pearl. You're the organiser!
Mason. You're supposed to be neutral!

*(**Pearl** blows a raspberry.)*

Look – get somebody else – I can't be the copper and the criminal!
Larry. We don't know what you did!
Mason. Then if you can't prove it – I'm free!
John. You've admitted it!

(Pause.)

Mason. The lady says she wants the *facts*!
John. You took it from Smith's Knife Shop.
Mason. Look – I'm not going to eliminate myself!
Larry. Where's Smith's Knife Shop?
Mason. Never heard of it. Ask her – she's said it, not me; I'm innocent till I'm proved guilty!
Pinky. You're w-windy!

(The public benches take up the chant 'windy'... and accompany it with a steady, continuous hand-clap.)

Mason. It ain't my job to tell you I'm guilty!
Larry. You've told us!
Mason. Prove it!
Larry. We'll make something up!

12

Mason. Thas all they do half the time anyway!
Larry. Somebody make something up against old Mason!
Mason. We've got to get a court for Miss Bryant!

(The chanting grows. 'Windy' has changed to 'guilty'.)

Larry. You're a menace to society!
Barry. He's a juvenile delinquent!
John. Hang him!
Mason. You're the Education!
Pearl. Flog him!
Mavis. Bring back the cat!
Mason. MIAOU! Look, Billie, tell them to shut up.
Billie. Why?
Mason. They've gone mad!
Billie. Nobody listens!

(He grabs her arm.)

Mason. Look, you know all about it –
Billie. DON'T TOUCH ME!

(The chanting continues.)

Mason *(bewildered).* We've got to get a court!
Glenda. Look – if this is supposed to be a court – help him – you know
  what it's like.
Billie. Thought you hated him!
Glenda. If I'm his mother – they're not giving him a chance!
Billie. THEY NEVER DO! NOBODY CARES! NOBODY!

(Absolute silence.)

They're like that lot. They don't care!

(Silence.)

Denise *(frightened).* Why not?

(Silence.)

Billie. They don't listen. You *took* that knife, didn't you?

(Pause.)

Mason. Yes.
Billie. Where from?
Mason. Dad.

(Pause.)

Billie. See, we're the same.
Mason. What?
Billie. Thieves.

(Pause.)

Mason *(soft)*. But I didn't get caught.

(Pause.)

What did you pinch?

(Pause.)

Denise *(deliberately)*. Give us the facts.

(Pause. **Billie** *marches into the witness box.)*

Billie *(defiant)*. W.P.C. Taylor, 'J' Division. At half-past four on Saturday, the second of November, I was called to Smith's Knife Shop, Little Lane, by Mr Havelock the manager who told me, in front of Billie, 'This girl has just been caught stealing this wall can-opener here in the shop.' I cautioned Billie and asked her if she had anything to say. She said no.

*(***Billie*** *steps down.)*

(to **Denise***)* You ask me if I want to ask the policewoman any questions.
Denise. Do you?

Billie. No. Now you ask me . . . why I did it.

(She steps up before the bench.)

Denise. Why did you take the −?
Pinky. Opener.
Denise. Billie?

(Pause.)

Denise. Say something.
Billie. To open tins.

(Silence.)

Denise *(incredulous)*. Is that what you said?

(Pause.)

Billie. No.
Denise. What did you say?
Billie. Nothing.
Denise. Then what?

(Pause.)

Billie. The magistrate said − if you steal a wall can-opener, there must be a reason. She asked my uncle who came with me, he was the only one who could because my mother can't move . . . she asked if he could help but he couldn't . . . we only see him Christmas-time, normally.
Pinky. Who's 'we'?
Billie. My mother. And me.
Pinky. Y-you can open tins with an ordinary t-tin opener.
Billie. She can't.

*(**Billie** sniffs.)*

Larry. Why can't you?
Billie. I have to come to school. Anyway, our one's blunt, and I can't grip.

15

(Pause.)

Denise. Then what did you want it for?

Billie. You ... haven't seen my mother trying opening a tin. Her ... hands, her fingers ... they're all twisted ...

(She sniffs back mounting emotion.)

... because of washing. She's oldish. The ends, of her fingers, they're like ... twigs.

(Pause.)

She can't put any pressure on. She can't grip. She has to have her lunch. So I ... I open the tins, ready. Then all she has to do is ... heat them up.

Denise. What about your dad?

(Silence.)

Mason. Didn't you tell all the judges this?

Billie. No.

Mason. Why not?

Billie *(fiercely)*. When I tried to tell the man in the shop he told me to shut up. Everybody tells everybody ... to shut up.

Denise. What did they do?

Billie. They should've given me a discharge. That's what you do first time! But they didn't. They told my uncle to bring me back in three weeks' time.

Denise. Why?

Billie. Because they didn't know anything about me. That's why I've been there twice.

(Pause.)

And they sent the Probation ... round to see my mother, and the Education people. And the Child Service. *(low)* They all came.

(Pause.)

16

Mason. Did they see your mum's . . . fingers?
Billie *(soft)*. Yes.

(Silence.)

Mason *(gently)*. Didn't they let you off . . . then?
Billie *(slowly)*. They said . . . her hands still didn't excuse the crime.
    The Welfare would do what they could. But I've got to pull my
    socks up. I've got to think of the worry I brought her. She cries
    a lot.
Denise. What did they give you?
Billie. Conditional discharge.
Pinky. Th-thas all right then.
Billie. It's a blot. My mother says it's a blot! She's ashamed! That's why
    she cries!

(Silence.)

    That's why you don't know what a cripple is!
Mason. Yes, well, I'm sorry, ain' I!
Denise. We're not . . .
Billie. What!
Denise. . . . ashamed of you.

(Silence. **Billie** *sniffs. The school bell rings. Door opens.)*

Miss Bryant. All right – away you go.

(No one moves.)

What on earth's happened?

(Silence. Outside, school sounds.)

    Mason?
Mason. Nothing, miss.

(Pause.)

Miss Bryant. Is this your knife?

17

(Pause.)

Mason. Yes, miss.
Billie. It's mine.

(Pause.)

Miss Bryant. The rest of you out!

(The class breaks up slowly. A door is slammed.)

Miss Bryant. Now. How did the court go?
Mason. All right, miss.
Miss Bryant. Who was on trial?
Mason. Me.
Billie. Me.

(Silence.)

Miss Bryant. Get rid of this, you stupid boy.

(She gives him the knife.)

And when you ... both have made up your mind who's on trial ...
I'd like to see it sometime.

(Pause.)

Out!

*(They rush out. The door slams. **Miss Bryant** opens a window, playground sounds flood in.)*

Five Green Bottles

THE CHARACTERS

GRAMP
MOTHER
KEVIN
DAVID
MAUREEN

FIVE GREEN BOTTLES

(An ordinary household. The play is set in the kitchen which is roomy and has access to the hall and living-room. The time of the play is that period of rush between 8 o'clock and 8.45 a.m. on any weekday.

Gramp *is reading the paper.* **Kevin** *is eating his toast. The radio is blaring cheery music.* **Mother** *is in the hall – calling upstairs.)*

Mother. David! It's eight o'clock. Are you coming down or aren't you! David!

David *(upstairs).* All right!

Mother. No 'all right' about it! Do you hear me!

David *(low).* Keep your hair on.

Mother *(going up a couple of steps).* What did you say?

David. I'm combing me hair down.

Mother. We'll have less of your lip, my lad. And I'm not calling you again. You'll be late. And tell that Maureen as well. *(Coming down the steps.)* Talk about a house of the dead.

David *(hammering on a door).* Maureen!

Mother *(shouting).* There's no need to shout!

David *(singing).* Maureen-O!

Mother. Maureen, you'll be late! *(pause)*

David. She's died in her sleep.

Mother. I give up.

(She comes back into the kitchen.)

Nobody can get up in this house – you must get it from your father. If I slept half as much as you lot do there'd be nothing done –

Kevin. The world'd fall to bits –

Mother. Kevin – get that telescope off the table –

Kevin. I'm looking at tomato cells.

Gramp. This paper's all creased!

21

Mother. Don't moan, Dad!

Gramp. It's like trying to read an elephant's kneecap!

Mother. Why've you left that piece of bacon?

Kevin. It's all fat.

Mother. You don't know what's good for you – it keeps out the cold –

Kevin. Why don't they make coats out of it, then?

Mother. That's enough. And turn that music down for heaven's sake – you can't even hear yourself think in a din like that.

Kevin. It's supposed to make you feel bright and breezy.

Mother. You must be joking. Turn it off.

(The radio is switched off.)

Oh! A bit of peace at last!

Gramp. Never had bacon when I went to school, never had bacon and . . . and . . . what're the other things?

Kevin. Eggs.

Mother. Now don't go on about it, Dad.

Gramp. Aye, eggs. Never. Just bread and jam and a four-mile walk.

Kevin. Aren't you glad you came to live with us, then?

Mother. Kevin, that's enough of that! There's a lot you youngsters today have to be thankful for and a full stomach's one of them.

Gramp. Just bread and jam and a five-mile walk.

Kevin. Four, you said.

Gramp. It might've been six if you count the hills.

Mother. There's many a starving Chinese who'd be only too glad to finish what you leave.

Kevin. Show me one.

Mother. Kevin, how many more times!

Gramp. Where're my glasses! I can't read without my glasses.

Kevin. The cat's wearing them.

Mother. Kevin!

Gramp. It's a plot!

Mother. Oh I don't know. If it's not one it's the other. What've I done wrong O Lord!

Gramp. The words go up and down without them!

Mother *(patiently)*. Where did you have them last, Dad?

Gramp. I had them just now.

Mother. Are you sitting on them?

Gramp. Don't be daft – why should I sit on them?

Mother. Stranger things've happened. Get up. Come on, get up.

(Gramp gets up. He's been sitting on them.)

There you are. What did I say?

Gramp. Who put them there, that's what I'd like to know!

Kevin *(low)*. The cat.

Mother. Do you want any more tea?

Kevin. No, thanks.

Gramp. Look, they're all twisted. You've got to have a head like a corkscrew to get them on now!

Mother *(calling)*. David! Maureen! I won't tell you again! It's ten past eight already!

Gramp *(reading out the headlines)*. 'BERLIN TABLE TALKS'. *(He giggles.)* Do you get it, young Kevin?

Kevin. Loud and clear.

Gramp. Berlin Table – talks!

Kevin *(low)*. Very funny!

Gramp. What d'you say?

Kevin *(loud)*. Very funny.

Gramp. Aye. *(mournfully)* Nobody laughs nowadays. That's the trouble with the world.

Mother. What were you and David quarrelling about last night?

Kevin. Nothing.

Mother. Nobody makes noise like that about nothing. Your dad's only got one ear and he heard it too. What was it?

Kevin. Nothing.

(He gets up.)

Mother. Where're you going?

Kevin. Get my books.

Mother. You still haven't answered my question, young man!

Kevin. It was nothing – honest!

Mother. Talk about blood from a stone. And take this telescope – I've only got one pair of hands.

(Letters come through the front door.)

There's the post.

23

(A door slams upstairs.)

David. I'll get them.
Mother. Those doors!
Kevin. I'll get them.
Mother. No, let David do it – it'll be one way of getting him downstairs.

*(***David*** *is cascading down stairs.)*

Kevin. It's always him.

(The living room door slams.)

Mother *(concerned)*. I hope it's about our Maureen's job. If it's not, she'll be so cut up.
Gramp. 'RENEWED FIGHTING IN SOUTH EAST ASIA'. It never stops.
Mother. I don't think it ever will.
Gramp. What's that?
Mother. War.
Gramp. You and the boys're always fighting –
Mother. That's different.
Gramp. Same drink, smaller bottle.

*(***David*** *comes slowly from the hall.)*

David. One for Dad ... one for Gramp. And the Pools thing.

(Pause.)

Mother. Nothing for our Maureen?
David. No, I looked.

(Pause.)

Mother. Well, let's keep our fingers crossed and hope something comes second post.
David. Here you are, Gramp.
Gramp. For me? *(afraid)* Who's writing to me? I bet it's money they're after –

24

Mother. Well, open it up and see.

Gramp. I'm a pensioner, not the Bank of England.

Mother. You've got enough to sink a battleship.

Gramp. A punt, maybe, but not a battleship.

(A door slams upstairs.)

Mother. Oh, those doors!

Maureen. Is that the post?

Mother. Yes.

Maureen. My letter there?

Mother. No, love. Nothing.

(Pause.)

Maureen. Oh. *(Pause.)* Too bad.

Mother. It might come with the second post, love.

Maureen. Pigs might fly an'all!

Mother. Now there's no call to think like that. I don't want you to give up!

Maureen. Oh, I'll be all right.

(A door slams upstairs.)

Mother. Those doors! *(Calling.)* And hurry up. Poor girl. She'd set her heart on that job.

David. What job?

Mother. If you'd pay attention to your sister for once in a while you'd know what job.

David. She don't think of us!

Mother. Do you want an egg?

David. How can you go to work on an egg – it'd crack.

Mother. I asked you a simple, straightforward question.

David. No thanks, just cereal.

Mother. At last!

(Cereal is shaken into a bowl.)

And help yourself to milk.

(Kevin enters.)

Kevin. Where've you put my books?
David *(mouth full)*. Nowhere.
Kevin. Come on –
David. Leave go! I haven't touched them!
Kevin. That's just the sort of dirty –
David. Watch it –
Kevin. Where did you put my books!
Mother. Will you two stop it!
Kevin. He's been and –
Mother. I mean it!

(Silence.)

Now let's get this straight once and for all. If you two can't get up in the morning without tearing each other's hair out – then at least have some consideration for other people.
Gramp. Like hiding their glasses.
Mother. I'm doing the talking, Dad. There's others in this house besides you. And I mean it. Now, both of you, hurry up and get out of my sight before I do something I'll be sorry for.

(She breaks an egg into a frying pan. It misses.)

Oh no! Quick, Kevin. A rag!

(Kevin's chair scrapes.)

Kevin. Use this!
Mother *(upset)*. Oh, look at it! All over the side! That's what come of listening to you two.
Kevin. Sorry, Mum.
Mother. It's all spoilt.

(Pause.)

David. I didn't want an egg.
Mother. It wasn't for you – it was for that Maureen.
Kevin. Do you know where my books are, Mum?

26

Mother. Mum, Mum, Mum – am I supposed to know everything?

Kevin. No, but –

Mother *(forced calm)*. If they're with the pinkish one with not many pages then they're all on the television.

David. You put them there before *Z-Cars*.

Kevin. Why don't you drop dead?

David. Dad can't afford the coffin.

Kevin. Pity.

Mother. On your way – and call that Maureen – she'll be late sure as eggs –

Kevin. Joke.

Mother. What does that mean?

Kevin. Eggs – sure as eggs.

Mother *(dawning)*. Oh, very funny – get a move on!

(Kevin goes into the hall.)

Kevin. Hey – Longlegs!

Maureen *(upstairs)*. What?

Kevin. It's twenty-to. If you hurry, you'll just be a half-hour late.

Maureen. I *am* hurrying.

Kevin. Mum's gone.

Maureen. Where?

Kevin. Rest home. Two little blokes in white coats're dragging her screaming out the back into an ambulance.

Maureen. Very clever.

Kevin. It's a quarter-to.

Maureen. It's not half-past!

(Kevin comes back into the kitchen.)

Kevin. She's alive.

Mother. Here's your tea.

David. Ta.

Mother. Thank you, not Ta.

David *(overdoing it)*. From the heart of my bottom – I thank you dear Mother.

Mother. Oh, what's the use?

Gramp *(shouting with wonder and excitement)*. They want me to play!

Kevin. Who – England?

Mother. Kevin!

Gramp. Bowls!

Kevin. Never heard of 'em.

Gramp. Kathy – they want me to bowl. Me!

Mother. When?

Gramp *(filled with awe)*. Tomorrow.

Mother. That's very nice. I'm glad. It'll mean a nice break for you, a change from just sitting around here.

Gramp. It's an ... honour.

Mother. Of course it is.

Gramp. After all ... I'm new to the game.

Mother. Dan says you're very good.

Gramp. You know, I never thought I'd do it!

Mother. If you don't stop jigging up and down you won't be able to – what're you sniggering at?

Kevin. Nothing.

Gramp. I'll have to get ready.

Mother. But it's not till tomorrow!

Gramp *(excited)*. What about my whites?

Mother. They're clean.

Gramp. And pressed?

Mother. And pressed.

Gramp. They must be ... knife edge. And my blazer? And my cravat? And my white pullover? And my handkerchief with the works crest on?

Mother. They're all ready, love.

Gramp. And my hockey cap.

Mother. You can't wear that!

(Pause.)

Gramp. Right, I think I'll go and clean my shoes –

Mother. Dad, they're like mirrors already.

Gramp. I must be ready. And I'll have an early night to be on the safe side.

Mother *(laughing)*. But it's still early morning.

Gramp. I'm very ... happy, my dear.

(He goes out.)

28

David *(whispering)*. He's crying!
Mother *(quietly)*. It means a lot to him.
Kevin. Why?
Mother. Just . . . because he's an old man.

(Pause.)

And give that Maureen a shake, Dad. *(calling)*

(But the old man is singing 'Underneath the Lamplight' and doesn't hear her.)

What're you so quiet about?
David. Can I have a black shirt, Mum?
Kevin. Here we go.
David. Shut up, you!
Kevin. Watch it!
David. Watch it yourself!
Mother. You two!!

(Silence.)

Why? Why do you want a black shirt?
David *(low)*. 'Cos . . . I want one.
Mother. And you always get what you want.
David. No.
Mother. Why then?
Kevin. 'Cos everybody else's got one!
Mother. I didn't ask you.
David *(helplessly)*. 'Cos I . . . just want one.
Mother. And you've got to be like everybody else, I suppose.
David. No.
Kevin. Yes.
David. No.
Mother. Oh, stop it, both of you. I can't be bothered with that now.
Off to school, you'll be late.

(Pause.)

David *(persistent)*. Can I have one?

29

Mother. No.

David. Why not?

Mother. It all costs money, that's why not. When I cough, 5p pieces don't drop out, you know.

David. All our lot in the form've got them.

(Kevin baas like a sheep.)

Mother. I bought you both a new white one only the other week. I'm not made of money. School rules say white shirts not black.

David. It's not for school!

Mother. No need to raise your voice ... Besides, you've got other shirts for best and for knocking around –

David. It's not for knocking around in.

Mother. Then what's it for?

(Gramp is now singing 'Marching Through Georgia' tunelessly.)

Come on, tell me.

David. I just *want* one.

Kevin. To wear to Gerry's.

Mother. Gerry's what?

Kevin. Party, Friday.

Mother. And all the others'll have them as well I suppose – you'll only want Mussolini there and you can start the Third World War.

David. I don't know what you're on about.

Mother *(soft)*. No – I don't suppose you do.

David. Then can I have one?

Mother. No. And that's final.

(Pause.)

You'll have to see your father.

(David bangs his teacup down.)

David. It's always the same!

(Enter Maureen in a hurry, in high heels.)

Maureen. What is?

David. Nothing.

Maureen. Do you know Gramp's cleaning his shoes on the landing? There's skits all over the wall.

Mother. Anything can happen this morning.

Maureen. Is that the time?

Mother. No, it's midnight. I've made you an egg –

Maureen. No, only tea.

Mother. Maureen!

Maureen. I'm sorry, I haven't got time.

Mother. And who's fault's that – you never eat.

Maureen. I'm all right.

(A cup is passed.)

That way I won't get fat. Ta.

David. Don't say 'ta', say 'thank you'.

Maureen. What's up with you all of a sudden?

David. Nothing.

Maureen. More milk, Mum, please, it's too hot.

Mother. David wants a black shirt. I can't afford it, neither can your father. He works hard enough as it is – he's got a family and a father to keep and that's strain enough on what he earns.

Maureen *(sipping)*. Oh, that's better. Oh, buy him one – or it'll be a guitar and bongo drums next time.

Mother. I've told you, I'm not made of –

David *(upset)*. All right!

Maureen. He never asks for anything, Mum, so this must be important if he asks for it.

Mother. I don't like disappointing anybody –

David. All right!!

Mother. But as it is I can't afford it!

Maureen. Skip it.

Mother. If it's that important, why don't you buy it?

Maureen *(half-angry)*. If I'd got that job I could afford it and I would.

David. I DON'T WANT IT NOW!

(Silence.)

Maureen *(softly)*. How much are they?

31

David. I don't want it.
Maureen. Five quid?

(Silence.)

Come on, silly.
David. I don't *want* it. *(pause)*
Kevin *(low)*. Four fifty.
Maureen. All right then.

(Pause.)

David. You will?
Maureen. Why not? Money comes, money goes. At least it'll make one
    person happy.
David. I'll pay you back thirty pence a week.
Maureen. Don't make promises.
David. I will.
Maureen. Then we'll get it tonight.
Mother. You don't have to give in to him, you know.
Maureen. Perhaps I want to.
Mother. It's your money.
Maureen. What about you, Kev? Do you want one as well?
David *(going into the hall)*. He won't, he said they're mad.
Kevin *(surly)*. I didn't.
David. You did last night!
Kevin. That was different!
Mother. So that's what all the noise was about.

(Pause.)

Maureen. Well, Kev? I haven't got all day.
Kevin. Can I have one too, please?

*(**David** baas like a sheep in the hall.)*

I'll thump you.
David. You're not big enough, ugly enough or old enough.
Kevin. Wanna try?
Mother. You two – out!

(They are both in the hall.)

Kevin. Thanks, Maur.
Maureen. Pleasure.
Mother. And don't forget your caps – you know what happened last
 time.
David. Thanks, Maur. Cheerio Mum. Cheerio Gramp!
Mother. Mind that door!

(It slams.)

Talk to the wall.

*(***Gramp** *starts singing 'Ten Green Bottles' on the stairs.)*

It only needed Dad to start!
Maureen. Change from his moaning. What's he so happy about?
Mother. He's in the bowling team tomorrow. Have you got time for
 another cup?
Maureen. I wonder who got that job.
Mother. Stop fretting.
Maureen. Who's fretting? I just feel I'm doing nothing where I am,
 that's all. I'm useless. Don't know why they keep me. They must
 like my legs.
Mother. Maureen.
Maureen. I'll just have to get married. And have quads. Four lots.
Mother. I wish you'd eat something.
Maureen. I'll have a doughnut come eleven.
Mother *(fondly)*. One minute she's talking of slimming, the next she's
 eating doughnuts ...
Maureen *(in the clouds)*. I shall die ... in my bed ... surrounded by
 half-nibbled doughnuts.
Mother. I don't want to rush you, but it's gone twenty-to.
Maureen. Oh, let them wait. I'm fed up.
Mother: Maureen!
Maureen. Come on – put your feet up – I only sit round till ten anyway.

(Chairs scrape.)

Mother. Oh, what it is to get your feet up!

33

Maureen. I never do anything else.

Mother. It was nice of you – about those shirts.

Maureen. Why?

Mother. Well, it obviously meant a lot to our David.

Maureen. I know.

Mother. Those two baffle me sometimes. You all do come to that. Kids. You have them, you raise them and then, one day, before you can turn round, you don't know them. They might as well be Zulus.

Maureen. The trouble with parents is they don't listen to what their children say.

Mother. Very clever.

Maureen. Some things're ... important.

Mother. Like black shirts?

Maureen. Might be.

Mother. Then God help the world.

Maureen. Our David's just twelve. He's changing ... that's why he's always doing his hair, why they fight, why they hate caps ... why they want different trousers – why they collect discs. It's all necessary. If they were Zulus – they'd ... I don't know – they'd be out killing a buffalo. To prove themselves. It's bound to happen

Mother. Quite a philosopher!

Maureen *(softly).* I'd give them anything ... anything as long as they don't end up ... just filling in petrol checks. Like me.

(Pause. She gets up.)

I'm off. It's going to rain.

Mother. It had to happen. I only cleaned the windows yesterday.

(Gramp enters.)

Gramp. Here. Found this by the front door. It's for you, Maureen.

Mother. Letter!

Maureen. It might be –

(Letter is torn open. Pause.)

I've got it! I've got the job!

Mother. Well, don't strangle me.

Gramp. Thought it might've been important.

Maureen. All the world's pink! Start next Tuesday.
Mother. There, what did I say!
Gramp. You playing bowls too then?
Maureen. Do you want a black shirt as well, Gramp, while I'm at it?
Gramp. You must be mad.
Maureen. I am.
Gramp. I always knew there was something about this house.
Mother *(pleased)*. Come on – hurry up, you've still got this job to finish.
Maureen. See you then!
Mother. Out!
Maureen. You smell of fried bread!
Mother. Out! And mind that door.
Maureen. 'Bye, Gramp.

(The door slams. Pause.)

Gramp. She didn't hear you.
Mother. Peace at last. It's like the Armistice when they've gone.
Gramp. And then there was one.
Mother. One what?
Gramp. Green bottle.
Mother. You're as mad as the rest of them. One day, they'll all come
　　down those stairs on time, they'll all eat together and quietly and
　　they'll all leave . . . *closing* the door behind them. Early.
Gramp. If they did, you wouldn't know what to do with yourself.
Mother. I'd die of shock, Dad, I know that for a fact. Stark staring
　　shock.

*(**Gramp** begins to sing 'Ten Green Bottles'.)*

　　Come on, out from under my feet. I've got this place to clean for
　　when the hordes return –
Gramp. I hope it doesn't rain . . .
Mother. It will.
Gramp. I can't bowl when the green's wet. Blast!
Mother. Now what's up?
Gramp *(like a child)*. I can't find my glasses.